More Animal Riddles

Who am I?

About the Author

Charlotte Sebag-Montefiore has been writing verse and lyrics for her friends for years. She started writing professionally for the children's website, *Storynory*. This is Charlotte's second book, and she tells us that there are lots more to come, and that the next one will be very different.

Charlotte Sebag-Montefiore

More Animal Riddles

Who am I?

Olympia Publishers
London

www.olympiapublishers.com
OLYMPIA PAPERBACK EDITION

ISBN: 978-1-78830-060-5

First Published in 2018
Olympia Publishers
60 Cannon Street
London
EC4N 6NP

Printed in Great Britain

Dedication

To my dear grandchildren: Lily, Hannah, Flora and Moshe

Acknowledgments

I acknowledge the help and support of my dear husband, Chris.

1

I do not walk as well as you
though my feet don't get cold.
They're webbed, which helps me swim along
I don't live to be old.

My feathers are quite waterproof
and so I don't get wet.
My children swim beside me,
do you know me yet?

My eggs are bigger than a hen's,
I think they are just right.
They make a lovely pastry,
a pastry nice and light!

I may live in your farmyard,
I may be wild and free.
I wish I weren't so tasty,
that you would not eat me!

When I'm wild I fly for miles,
away from cold and snow.
I must have water for my food
it's to wetlands that I go!

Now dear child, you've listened,
just tell me what's my name.
If you don't know, don't worry
I'll tell you all the same.

2

I have some cousins who are whales,
I like the water too.
It cools me down when I'm too hot,
it does the same for you!

I am so much in the water
that I have a funny head.
My eyes and nose are at the top
yes – that is what I said!

I can hear under water.
I see quite well down there.
I hold my breath for such a time,
you hunt us, it's not fair.

My body's like a barrel.
When frightened, I attack.
I can outrun you easily,
so you should watch your back!

For people I'm a danger.
Our teeth are good at crunching,
they're very sharp and what is more
they're very good at munching!

Now dear child, you've listened,
just tell me, what's my name.
If you don't know, don't worry
I'll tell you all the same.

3

You've seen me in the country,
I don't live in the town.
Some of us, at any rate,
have two horns for a crown.

We're herbivores, and ruminate.
We like to chew the cud.
Our stomach has four different parts.
We do not mind the mud!

We do not like it on our own,
we like to live in herds.
You love us for our creamy milk
you use for cheese and curds!

We have to eat a lot of grass
and drink a lot as well.
On mountainsides, we sometimes have
a little tinkle bell!

Our males are very, very strong,
they are aggressive too.
Don't wear red, they might attack
toss, hurt or damage you!

Now dear child, you've listened,
just tell me, what's my name.
If you don't know, don't worry
I'll tell you all the same.

4

My brothers or my sisters,
we can be twenty-five.
We have a nasty bite from birth
as soon as we're alive!

I am beautiful and lovely,
I slide with slithery grace.
You may not even see me,
I could be any place.

I can change my colour
on a hunt for food to eat.
The one thing that is certain is
that what I like is meat!

Meat I simply have to have.
Rats, bats, a squirrel, deer.
My mouth will open, oh so wide,
a sight to inspire fear!

When I'm born, I'm not so small.
When grown, I'm very long.
I like to give a lovely hug
to death, I am so strong!

Now children, you have listened,
just tell me, what's my name.
If you don't know, don't worry,
I'll tell you all the same.

5

My stripes are quite unique.
Your fingers have their prints.
There is nothing quite the same
either before or since!

My stripes have an advantage,
they send away the flies.
Insects do not like them,
they buzz off to the skies!

My stripes will also keep me cool.
I run fast and it's hot.
Savannah's where I may be found,
we like our herds a lot!

They're thousands of us sometimes!
That makes me safer too.
We zigzag when we're hunted,
by animals or you.

If one of us is wounded,
one bad unlucky day,
the others circle round to help
drive predators away.

Now dear child, you've listened,
just tell me, what's my name.
If you don't know, don't worry
I'll tell you all the same.

6

We really are quite clever.
We're able to use tools.
We can get food out from your traps,
we're definitely not fools!

I find the way much better
than a woman or a man.
We like to eat fish, meat and plants
and honey if we can!

I don't forget an animal.
I remember them for years.
I run much faster than you think,
My skin – it has two furs!

Our legs are bowed for balance, grip
– we can also walk upright.
I can be different colours,
either black, or brown or white!

In Russia, we're a symbol
of power and of strength.
Our claws are shaped for what they do
for digging they need length!

Now dear child, you've listened,
just tell me what's my name.
If you don't know, don't worry
I'll tell you all the same.

7

The Romans brought us to the north,
from deserts where it's hot.
We know where it is safe to tread,
we won't go where it's not!

You may think this is stubborn,
but you might find you are glad.
We trust you to protect us,
we'll save you from what's bad.

We've been your beasts of burden
for several thousand years.
We can hear sounds from afar
for we have such big ears!

We are not picky eaters,
we keep the dogs away.
Waterproof our fur is not,
we hate a rainy day

We do not like to be alone,
that is not our way.
You'd know for sure that I am me
if you could hear my bray!

Now dear child, you've listened,
just tell me, what's my name.
If you don't know, don't worry
I'll tell you all the same!

8

We're small and run fast on the ground
or even up a tree.
We twitch our tails to say "Watch out",
you'll not catch up with me!

Our eyes are high up in our heads
so we can see all round
We run in zigzags to escape
so that we can't be found!

We may hang mushrooms out to dry.
Yes, that is really true.
So there are ways in which we are
just the same as you.

We fatten up on nuts and things
and squirrel food away
in different places, then come back
to eat it up one day!

Our tail acts as a parachute
to slow us if we fall.
But we are such good jumpers
That we rarely slip at all!

Now dear child you've listened,
just tell me what's my name.
If you don't know, don't worry
I'll tell you all the same.

9

I like to live in groups like you.
We're mammals in the sea.
My blowhole help us breathe the air,
why don't you play with me?

I like to jump and ride the waves
and oh, I have such fun!
We'll help each other if need be,
and you and everyone!

We bring our children up quite well
and teach them what to do.
How to use the tools they can,
as your parents teach you!

I put a sponge upon my nose
so it will not get sore,
looking for the food I need
when I need some more.

I orient with radar
and liaise with a friend,
to let them know just where I am
with signals that I send!

Now dear child you've listened,
just tell me, what's my name.
If you don't know, don't worry
I'll tell you all the same!

10

We've eight long limbs with tentacles,
a beak to crack the shell
of crabs and mussels which we like.
Oh we eat very well!

We like to play – that takes brains.
We're really rather clever.
We spray our predators with ink
so they can't see us ever!

We squeeze into tight spaces
– oh we can swim quite fast.
We need to keep ourselves quite safe
when predators swim past!

Our sense of touch and eyesight,
both are very good.
We lay two hundred thousand eggs,
they'd grow up if they could!

I told you we are clever
we can communicate.
We use our limbs to unscrew jars,
learn to manipulate!

Now dear child, you've listened,
just tell me, what's my name.
If you don't know, don't worry
I'll tell you all the same!

11

A kind of mongoose, hey, that's me
I can be wild or tame.
I like to catch the rats and mice
the taste is much the same!

My eyes are large with darkish fur,
my face is long not round.
My long sharp claws dig out my home
in burrows underground.

It's cooler there out of the heat
and safer with my friends.
We've many doors and entrances,
straight tunnels without bends.

We babysit each other's pups
while others hunt for food.
Rival clans are dangerous
they try to kill our brood.

We have a sentry posted
to keep watch in the sky.
If danger comes, he squeals – we hide
in boltholes dug nearby.

Now dear child, you've listened,
just tell me, what's my name.
If you don't know, don't worry
I'll tell you all the same.

12

We're lumbering, galumphing,
we're certainly not small.
We do our fighting with our heads,
we're very big and tall!

Our eyesight's poor, we're colour blind,
our world looks pretty grey.
Our smell and hearing's very good
we find our food that way.

We're mostly mild and gentle
unless we're with our calves.
Then we'll attack you humans
we don't do things by halves

Never ever feed us,
it is against the law.
We'll hurt you when we meet again
and press you for some more.

Our young have antler bumps from birth.
We've lots of triplets, twins.
When we lick our lips take care,
we've kicking in our shins!

Now children you have listened,
just tell me what's my name.
If you don't know, don't worry
I'll tell you all the same.

13

We used to go about by day
we would do if we could.
We changed our habits when you came
adaptable is good!

Because of this, we've done quite well.
Our numbers have increased,
and so we live in cities too,
where we're the tip-top beast!

What do I eat? 'Most anything
whatever I can get.
Fish and froggies, snakes and deer...
be careful of your pet!

At night together in our pack,
beneath a starry sky,
we like to sit and howl and yelp
"Yi yippee yippee yi!"

We hunt by smell or vision,
in winter in a pack.
It makes us more effective
so food we do not lack!

Now dear child, you've listened,
just tell me what's my name.
If you don't know, don't worry,
I'll tell you all the same!

14

I am a champion reptile
I have a pretty hiss.
My breath is pretty smelly too
I am not nice to kiss!

My tongue is very, very long
it darts out here and there.
So keep your distance, do look out,
I could be anywhere.

We hunt by patience, and by stealth,
eat fresh or rotten meat.
We trot along quite rapidly
and then we snap at feet!

Our prey will weaken slowly,
we follow and we wait.
Our poisoned nips will do for them
they can't avoid their fate.

We are not like your mothers,
we may eat our own young.
They climb up to avoid us
or roll themselves in dung.

Now dear child, you've listened
just tell me, what's my name.
If you don't know, don't worry
I'll tell you all the same

15

I am a North American,
– no stripes and never spots.
My fur is thick and wonderful.
I eat meat lots and lots!

I'm big and eat ten pounds a day.
I'm lean with little fat.
I like to have a deer for lunch
a moose, something like that!

I have a lovely throaty purr
that means I am nearby.
I might be closer than you think,
jumping in the sky!

For I jump up some sixteen feet
it's more along the ground.
Forty-five, that's really far
I land without a sound.

I'm faster than the other beasts,
that's how I catch my prey.
I jump and pounce, it is such fun
and they can't run away!

Now dear child, you've listened
just tell me, what's my name.
If you don't know, don't worry
I'll tell you all the same!

16

I'm big and built to stand the cold,
I can get rather hot.
It doesn't suit me running fast,
I would much rather not.

My neck is long and helps
me find yummy fish to eat.
My tail is short, my ears are small,
I think they're rather sweet!

I'm white and have two layers of fur
I need to have some fat.
I cover up my little nose
if I'm cold in spite of that.

We learn to hunt and trap as well.
It's hard to catch a seal.
We like to rub each other's nose
in friendship at a meal!

Now the planet's warming
it isn't good for me.
I might float off upon some ice,
I might go out to sea.

Now dear child, you've listened
just tell me, what's my name.
If you don't know, don't worry
I'll tell you all the same!

17

The other birds don't like us.
They know what we can do.
They group and try to drive us off
"Fly off! Oh shoo, shoo, shoo!"

My mum is very clever.
Her thick eggs do not break
when they are dropped in others' nests
they look the same, they're fake!

I make sure I hatch the first.
I eat and grow quite big,
then tip the other nestlings out
I do not care a fig!

I must build up my strength, you see.
I have to fly away.
To Africa, that's where we go,
it is so far away.

Someone always says they're first
to hear my voice this year.
When I sing, the people hum,
they know that spring is here.

Now dear child, you've listened
just tell me, what's my name.
If you don't know, don't worry
I'll tell you all the same!

18

People thought we were a hoax,
that we could not be true.
We're monotremes, for we lay eggs
though mammals, just like you!

Except you have no fur or beak,
you cannot seal your nose.
You have no webbing on your feet
but only little toes!

We do not need a dentist,
we've no teeth when we're grown.
We use our skin as goggles,
that's rare, but not unknown.

We swim under the water,
scoop crawlies with our bill,
plus a bit of gravel,
it helps us chew our fill!

We use our feet and tail to steer.
We go about at night.
We use our feet to dig our homes,
we rest there when it's light!

Now dear child, you've listened
just tell me, what's my name.
If you don't know, don't worry
I'll tell you all the same!

19

We're sociable and live in groups.
We hop and jump all day,
we have such powerful big hind legs
that we can hop away!

I have one baby every year
I keep it in my pocket,
and feed it different kinds of milk
until it wants to hop it!

I go months without water,
move forward, never back.
When there's a drought, I'm lucky
for I don't feel the lack.

The wolves are gone, thank goodness.
You hunt us now instead.
We eat the grass your cattle want,
you'd rather have us dead!

We are not birds or mammals
our ears can swivel round.
Because of this our hearing's good
as we hear every sound.

Now dear child, you've listened
just tell me, what's my name.
If you don't know, don't worry
I'll tell you all the same!

20

We're beautiful, of course.
We glide with grace along.
The biggest on the water,
we have a famous song!

Sometimes we are black.
In Europe we are white.
We're strong, and we could break your arm
if we should have a fight!

We're great birds in the air.
We do need space to fly.
Once we're up, we're very fast.
We're lovely in the sky!

Our feathers – we have thousands,
twenty, twenty-five.
We're faithful and we pair just once
as long as we're alive!

We're herbivores in general.
Alas you like our meat.
Royal banquets by tradition
served us as good to eat!

Now dear child, you've listened
just tell me, what's my name.
If you don't know, don't worry
I'll tell you all the same!

21

I am not a dog as such.
I'm wild and not a cat.
My fur is warm and pretty
you farm us just for that!

My mum and dad, maybe my aunt
will help me when I'm small.
When I am born, I'm helpless
can't see or smell at all.

We hunt and scavenge for our meat,
eat berries, birds and mice.
We can live almost anywhere
we eat that which tastes nice!

Like you, I sometimes store supplies
if I've more than I need.
It saves me from real hunger
and I can have a feed.

My whiskers on my legs and face
do help me find my way.
Don't forget I like to hunt
by night and not by day!

Now dear child, you've listened
just tell me what's my name.
If you don't know, don't worry
I'll tell you all the same.

22

It's true, there can be lots of us
once we find a place
with luscious grass that's safe to eat,
we do like lots of space!

Our tail is just the perfect size.
It's very short and sweet.
So predators can't catch it,
they'd find me good to eat!

If danger's there, we tell our friends,
we thump hard on the ground.
Our long ears help us hear the news,
what's happening all around!

We're social and affectionate
communicate by sounds.
You sometimes keep us as your pets
we jump by leaps and bounds!

We really are good jumpers
on grass, or mud or sand.
We push off from our great big feet,
they don't slip when we land!

Now child, you have listened,
just tell me what's my name.
If you don't know, don't worry
I'll tell you all the same.

23

I am big and powerful,
I need a lot to eat.
At night, I may hunt with my friends,
we have to find some meat.

A hippo, or an elephant
a juicy, tender treat.
We may take food from other beasts,
we have to find some meat.

In fact, our ladies hunt the most,
defend our lands, what's ours.
We're first to eat our fill of meat,
I can sleep twenty hours.

You'll hear my roar a long way off
and know me by my mane.
I'll take another's woman,
that means I'll kill again!

I need to kill her children
and her ex too, you see.
I need to have young that are mine
My woman is for me.

Now child, you have listened,
just tell me what's my name.
If you don't know, don't worry
I'll tell you all the same.

24

You call us lots of filthy names,
so undeserved – oh why?
Even our young babies
don't dirty where they lie!

We're clever as a three-year-old,
communicate the same.
We do not talk but oink and grunt
and we can learn our name!

We roll in mud to keep quite cool.
You sweat more than we do.
You say we're sweaty but we're not,
in fact we're quite like you!

We will eat almost anything,
no matter what the taste.
Simply give us lots and lots
we do not like to waste!

We're friendly and we're sociable
we like to lie together.
A lovely heap with all our friends
no matter what the weather!

Now child, you have listened,
just tell me what's my name.
If you don't know, don't worry
I'll tell you all the same.

25

I love the wild places
I need to feel quite free.
My sense of smell is very good
and helps me hunt, you see!

For small prey, I will hunt alone.
We're stronger in a pack.
It's better for the bigger beasts,
a moose, perhaps a yak!

With two layers, how my fur sticks up
on a winter's bitter night.
In summer, my fur lies quite flat,
I always feel just right!

My stamina is very good,
it is part of my power.
I can run very fast as well
some sixty miles an hour!

In the food chain, we are high,
but you present a threat.
We thought we might become extinct,
it hasn't happened yet!

Now dear child, you have listened,
just tell me, what's my name.
If you don't know, don't worry,
I'll tell you all the same…

26

My fangs are hinged with poison
I can be eight feet long.
A triangle – that is my head,
the rattle is my song!

Our rattle's made of keratin
just like a fingernail.
Other snakes can't hear it
it works, though, without fail!

Lizards, tasty rodents,
I wait and feel their heat.
I rise and strike like lightning, fast,
– oh they're so nice to eat!

In North and South America
that is where we're found.
Deserts, scrub and rocky hills
that's where we go to ground.

If it's cold, we hibernate.
We do not if it's hot.
We keep our den for decades
we're safe there, like as not.

Now dear child, you have listened,
just tell me, what's my name.
If you don't know, don't worry,
I'll tell you all the same...

27

I fly but I am not a bird,
I am a mammal too.
In fact I am the only one
to fly. You can't, can you?

Upside down's the way I sleep.
For me, that's where it's at.
You humans are so funny!
You like to sleep quite flat!

Some of us have great big wings,
we have a nasty bite.
We can infect you, when we do,
we like to fly at night!

When we're cold, we may fly off
to somewhere where it's not.
Blood we eat and insects,
we do eat such a lot.

We send off sounds that bounce away
from everything indeed.
Returning echoes coming back
tell us all we need.

Now dear child, you've listened,
just tell me, what's my name.
If you don't know, don't worry,
I'll tell you all the same…

28

I wish I ate royal jelly,
then I could be the Queen,
with luxury and royal perks,
that is what I mean!

The boys, good only for one thing,
are lazy, lie about.
Come winter, when the food gets scarce,
we simply throw them out.

We girls are busy in our home,
we're necessary workers!
We are not like the boys at all,
the drones, they're idle shirkers!

We're vital to life on this earth.
We pollinate the plants.
They attract us with their nectar,
our flight a graceful dance.

We are the only insects
that make some food for you.
Delicious and nutritious,
we think so – you do too!

Now dear child, you've listened,
just tell me, what's my name.
If you don't know, don't worry,
I'll tell you all the same…

29

Simplicity is good.
Who wants complications?
I'm ancient, living in the sea,
I float for my sensations!

I'm mostly made of water.
We do have eyes galore
to help us see just everything.
We may have twenty-four!

I need to see what I can eat,
what threatens to eat me.
I've many arms to stuff my food
into my mouth for free!

Some of us have eight arms
and some of us have four.
Each helps us to swallow
some plankton, fish and more!

Our tentacles lilt in the sea,
they have a nasty sting.
So watch out, for the currents
make us sway and swing!

Now dear child, you've listened,
just tell me, what's my name.
If you don't know, don't worry,
I'll tell you all the same...

30

I live high in the Andes,
I carry heavy packs.
If loads are just too heavy,
I'll sit, not strain my back!

My ears are like bananas,
curve inwards, as you see.
I'm trainable, domestic
and sociable, that's me!

The Incas found us vital,
we do not lick our young.
Instead we hum and nuzzle them.
The Incas used our dung.

They prized our lovely wool and hides,
we're peaceable and calm.
But when we're cross, then we will spit.
We keep the sheep from harm!

We kick out at coyotes,
we like to live in herds.
Alpacas are our cousins,
there's no smell from our turds!

Now dear child, you've listened,
just tell me, what's my name.
If you don't know, don't worry,
I'll tell you all the same…

31

Life is very hard for us.
We lay four thousand eggs.
We start off in freshwater
and then we grow some legs!

People change throughout their life
but we change even more.
When grown, we hop upon the land,
we don't do that before!

Birds with vicious beaks, and snakes,
fishes eat me too.
Camouflage and climbing helps,
you people eat me too!

Our tongues – they catch us insects.
They're fastened in the throat.
Out they whip to catch our food,
that is how we hunt!

Because we need the water,
we don't like snow and ice.
Somewhere wet and warm is good
that is really nice!

Now dear child, you've listened.
Just tell me, what's my name.
If you don't know, don't worry,
I'll tell you all the same...

32

You used us for so many things
for farming, hunting, war.
You race us now for pleasure
you did that too before.

We animals lived in a herd,
we're better in a group.
We're herbivores, sleep standing up,
we're OK in a troop!

We're very fast, good jumpers
we need to work with you.
Our hooves are like your fingernails
please trim them, oh please do!

Our eyes are placed so they can see
what's coming up behind.
That's useful for survival
and it's good to bear in mind!

Our ears reveal our feelings,
they move far more than yours.
Our teeth keep growing all our lives
the tough grass is the cause!

Now dear child, you've listened
just tell me, what's my name.
If you don't know, don't worry,
I'll tell you all the same…

33

In our youth, we're grey or brown,
we're pinker when we're old.
We've got some lovely tusks for teeth
we're happy in the cold.

Mustachio'd, with whiskers,
hundreds, you should know,
they're sensitive, and help us find
our food, so down we go!

Right down to the ocean floor
we can hold our breath.
For thirty minutes – but not more
or we could meet with death!

Sea cucumbers and mussels,
that's what we like to eat.
Clams as well, soft coral,
oh how we like some meat!

You used to hunt us for our tusks
our fat and blubber too.
We are endangered carnivores
we've never hunted you!

Now dear child, you've listened,
just tell me, what's my name.
If you don't know, don't worry,
I'll tell you all the same...

34

We've many different cousins,
the otter, wolverine,
weasels and some others
that you may not have seen.

I'm stocky and my legs are small,
you may see me at night.
My head is long, my ears are short,
my face is black and white!

We're very good at digging.
That's why we have long claws.
We sharpen them upon a tree
not far from our front doors!

We live in groups, some six of us,
our home is underground.
We line our beds with grass and leaves,
it's comfy, we have found!

We are nocturnal, with poor sight,
we hunt by sound and smell.
Birds and lizards, rodents too
we eat some veg as well!

Now dear child, you've listened,
just tell me, what's my name.
If you don't know, don't worry,
I'll tell you all the same…

35

We date back to the dinosaurs,
reptiles from long ago.
We tuck our heads into our shell,
it protects us, did you know?

My skeleton includes my shell
with forty bones or more.
It's part of me, does not come off
grows with me, that's for sure.

Our lifespan can be very long.
Some of us eat meat.
Most of us live in the sea.
Some think we're good to eat!

But water, oh we like it,
though we lay our eggs on land.
We clamber to a pleasant spot
and lay them in the sand.

In some of us, the temperature
determines what we'll be.
A boy if it is colder,
if it's warm, a girl we'll see!

Now dear child, you've listened,
just tell me, what's my name.
If you don't know, don't worry,
I'll tell you all the same...

36

We are quite amazing.
One meal a year's enough
to keep us from starvation,
for we are very tough.

If this has not convinced you,
I'll have to try again.
Time in the freezer's very cold
but leaves us right as rain!

Our painful poison's famous
but mostly will not kill you.
It may be used in medicine,
served at banquets just to thrill you!

Our stinging tail curves nicely round,
can kill and paralyze.
We can kill in other ways,
eat our prey as it dies.

Our mothers give us help and care
we may not have a dad.
We've eight legs, but Mum carries us
for four weeks – that's not bad.

Now dear child, you've listened,
just tell me, what's my name.
If you don't know, don't worry,
I'll tell you all the same…

ANSWERS

1: Duck
2: Hippo
3: Cow
4: Boa Constrictor
5: Zebra
6: Bear
7: Donkey
8: Squirrel
9: Dolphin
10: Octopus
11: Meerkat
12: Moose
13: Coyote
14: Komodo Dragon
15: Cougar
16: Polar Bear
17: Cuckoo
18: Platypus
19: Kangaroo
20: Swan
21: Fox
22: Rabbit
23: Lion
24: Pig
25: Wolf
26: Rattlesnake
27: Bat

28: Bee
29: Jellyfish
30: Llama
31: Frog
32: Horse
33: Walrus
34: Badger
35: Turtle
36: Scorpion

If you have enjoyed these riddles,
read Charlotte Sebag-Montefiore's first book of
animal riddles in verse.

Charlotte Sebag-Montefiore

Who am I?